Wind an

Part 1

story by Jeremy Strong

illustrated by Ken Stott

The wind had blown hard all day.
It bent the trees in the park.
It rattled the tiles on the roofs.

It was too wet and windy
to go outside.
Jojo and Mouse played indoors.

Ben helped his mum.
"What a horrible day!"
she said.

Sam made a camp under the table.
"No rain in here," she smiled.

Night came and the wind
howled in the dark.
The trees banged against
the windows.
It was hard to sleep.

In the middle of the night
the great storm came.
Thunder crashed.
Lightning split the sky.

The wind tore through
the darkness.

Bins were blown over.
Windows were broken.
Plants were snapped in half.

11

The drains were full of water.
A river of rain ran down
Story Street.

In the park the wind hit the
trees like a giant fist.
A big tree groaned and cracked.
It began to fall.

Crash!

The tree hit the play park.

Smash!
It crushed the little shop
that sold ice cream.

The shop was smashed.

Wires were snapped.

Sparks jumped from the wires.

Soon a little fire had started.
Tiny flames licked the ground.

The fire spread, moving
through the broken shop.

Paper began to burn.

The flames were getting bigger.

Now the fire was a
hungry monster.
The flames ate anything
that got in their way.

The thunder still roared
and the wind still howled.

The noise of the storm woke Ben.

He looked out of his window.

He saw flames in the park.

Ben ran to his mum and dad.
They were fast asleep.
Ben shook them hard.
"Wake up! Wake up!
There's a fire!"

Mr King jumped out of bed.
He rang the fire station.
"There's a fire in the park!"
he said. "Come quickly!"